tv themes

Music arranged and processed by Barnes Music Engraving Ltd
East Sussex TN22 4HA, UK

Cover design by xheight Limited

Published 1996

© **International Music Publications Limited**
Southend Road, Woodford Green, Essex IG8 8HN, England

BLIND DATE

By LAURIE HOLLOWAY

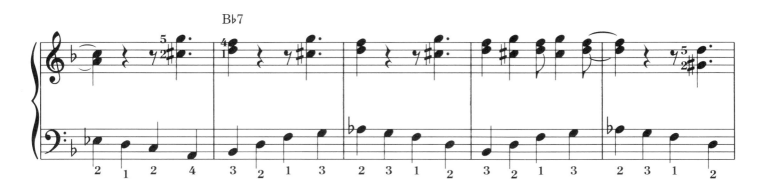

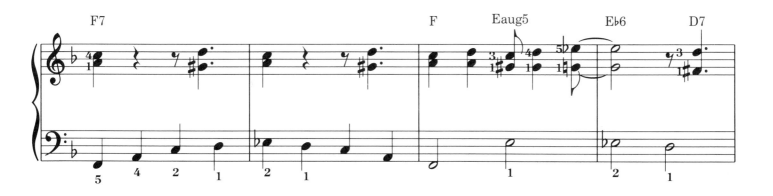

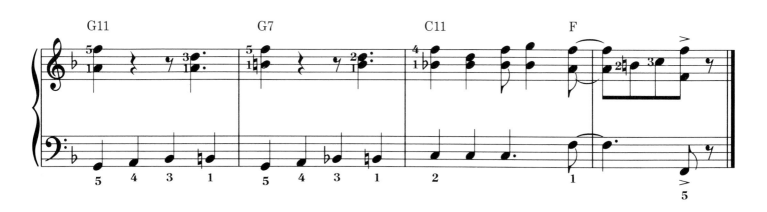

BEVERLY HILLS, 90210
(Main Theme)

By JOHN E DAVIS

Moderato

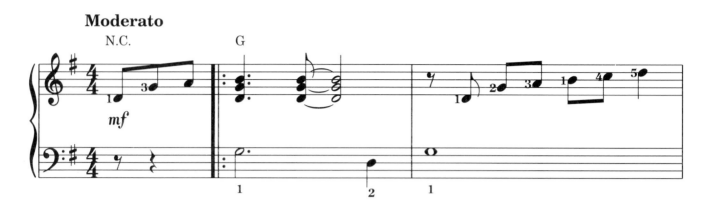

CHEERS
(Where Everybody Knows Your Name)

Words and Music by
GARY PORTNEY and JUDY HART ANGELO

Slow ballad

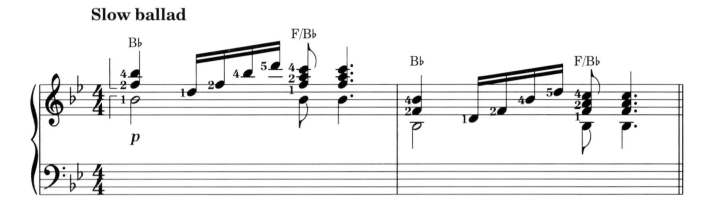

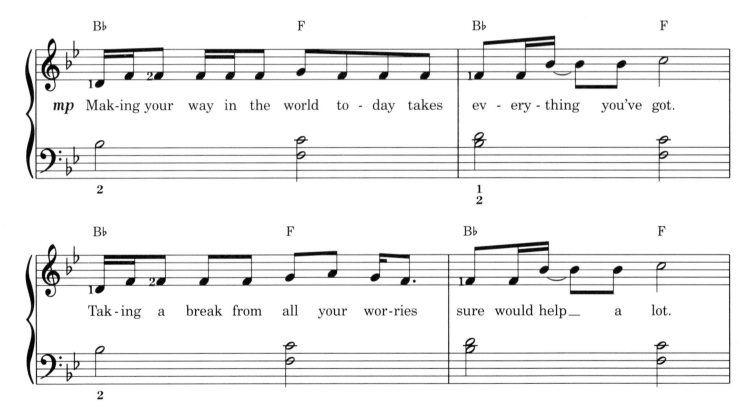

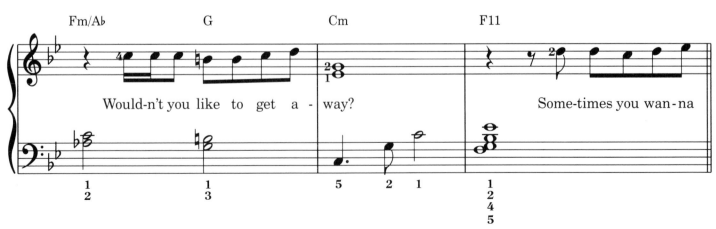

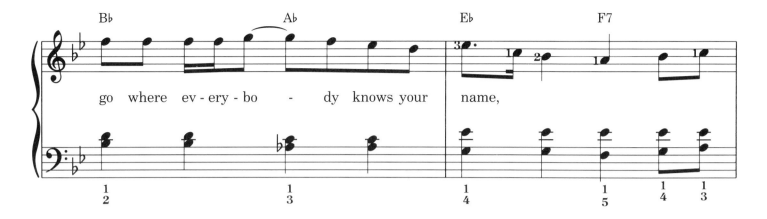

go where ev - ery - bo - dy knows your name,

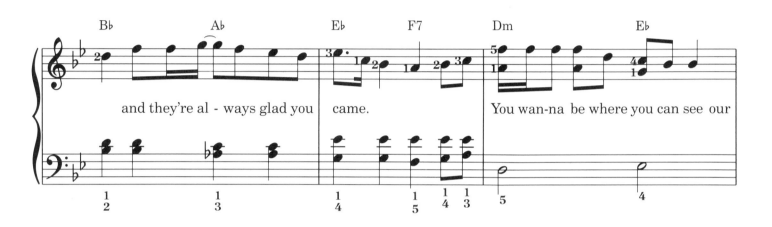

and they're al - ways glad you came. You wan-na be where you can see our

trou-bles are all the same. You wan-na go where ev - ery - bo - dy knows

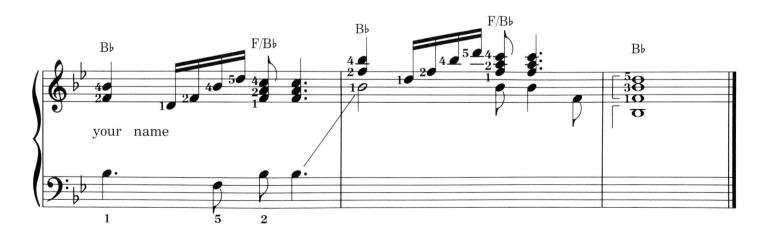

your name

CHICAGO HOPE

By MARK ISHAM

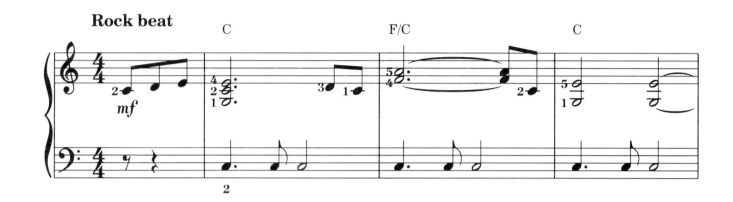

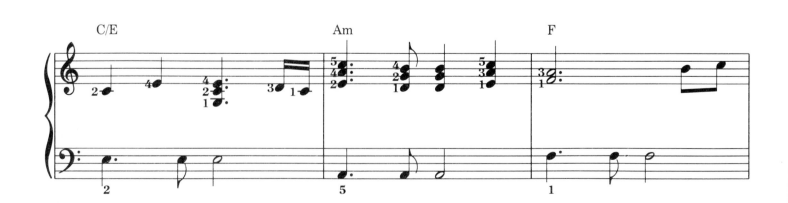

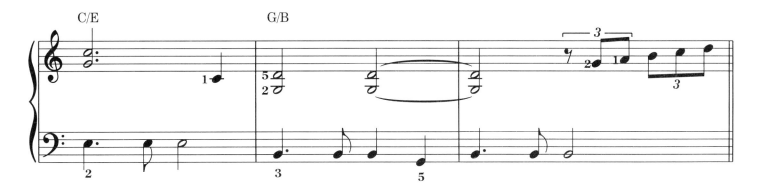

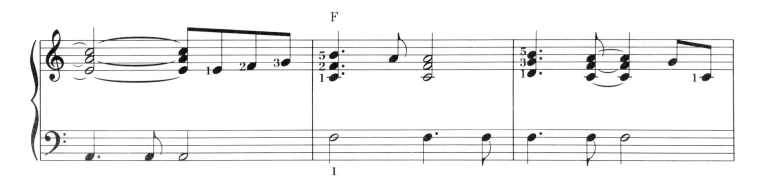

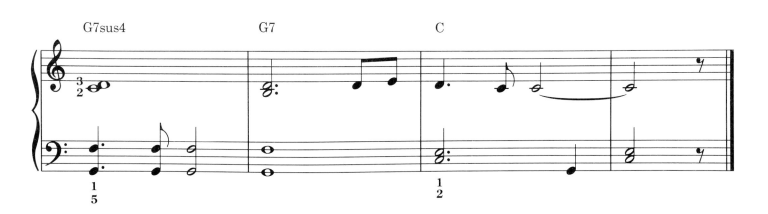

CORONATION STREET

By ERIC SPEAR

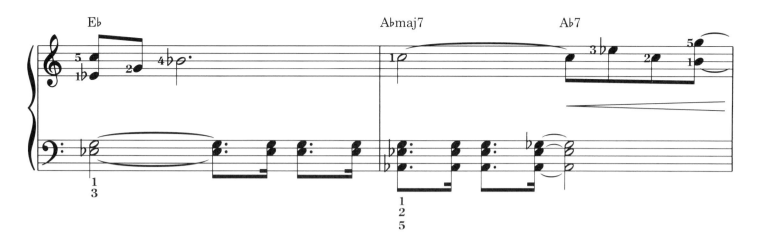

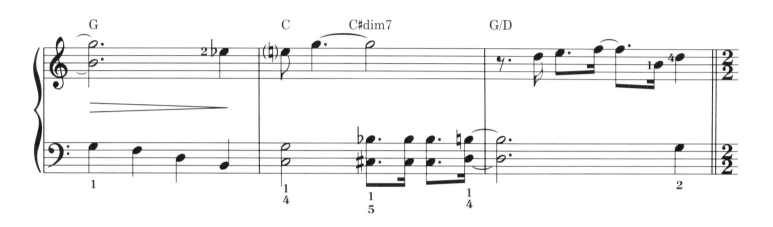

Rubato

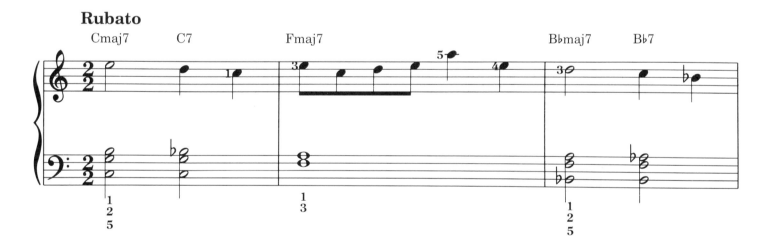

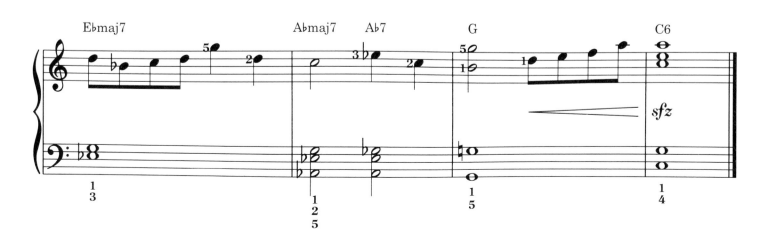

DANGERFIELD

By NIGEL HESS

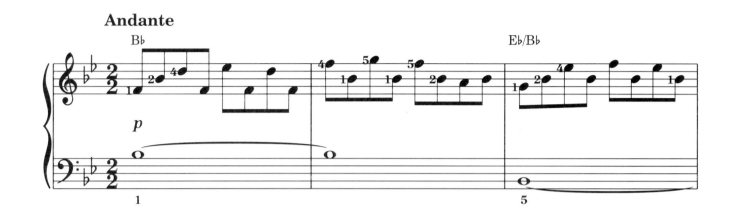

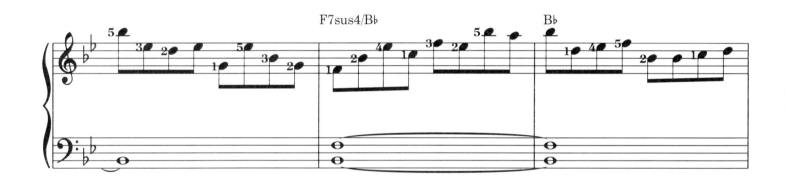

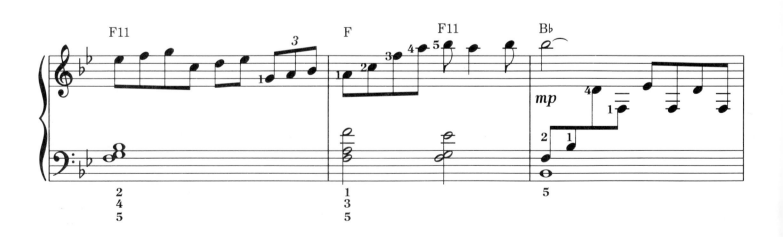

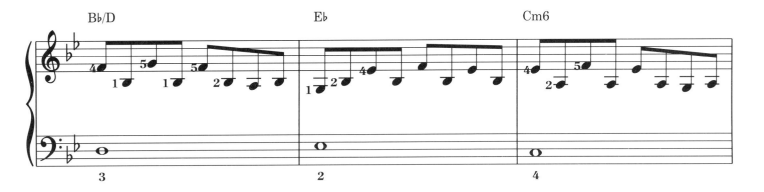

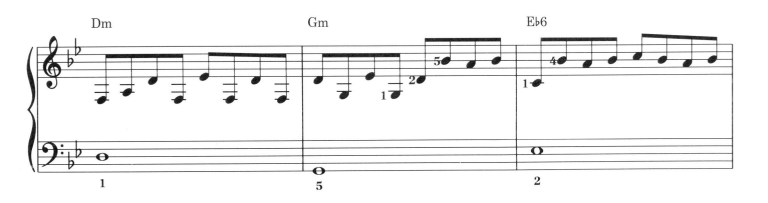

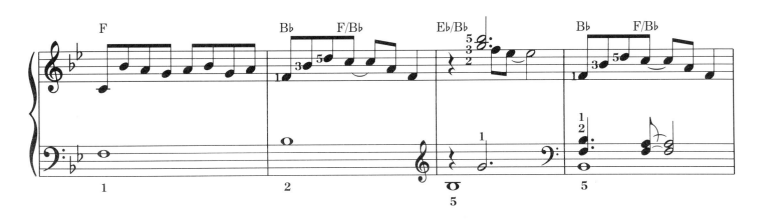

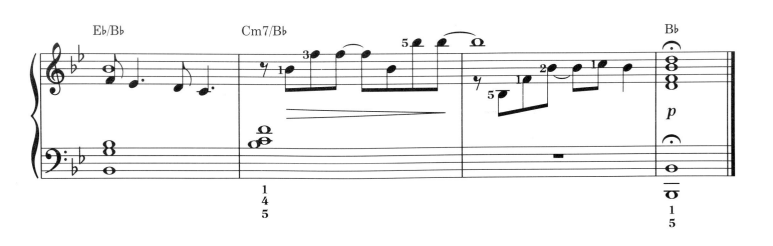

EASTENDERS

By LESLIE OSBORNE
and SIMON MAY

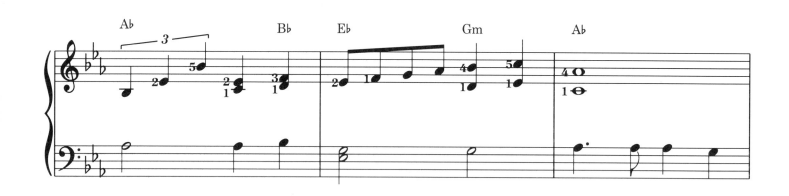

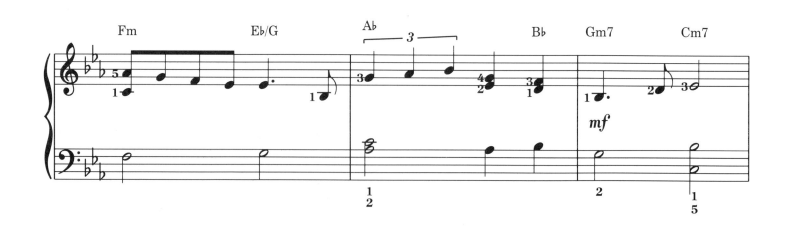

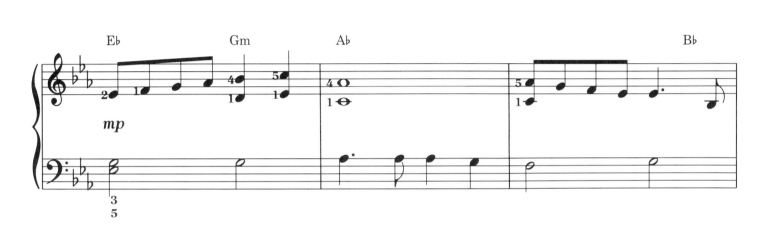

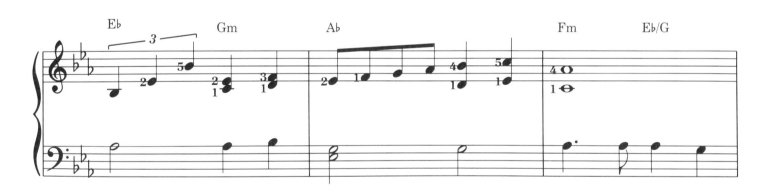

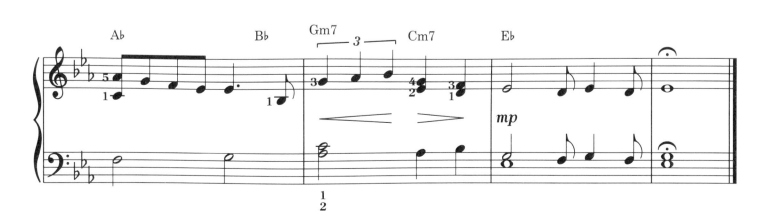

FILM '96
(I Wish I Knew How It Would Feel To Be Free)

Words by BILLY TAYLOR and DICK DALLAS
Music by BILLY TAYLOR

FRIENDS
(I'll Be There For You)

Words and Music by DAVID CRANE, MARTA KAUFFMAN,
PHIL SOLEM, DANNY WILDE and ALLEE WILLIS

Fast Rock

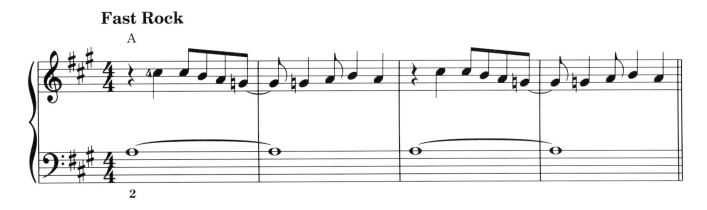

So no-one told___ you life___ was gon-na be___ this way.

Your job's___ a joke,___ you're broke,___ your

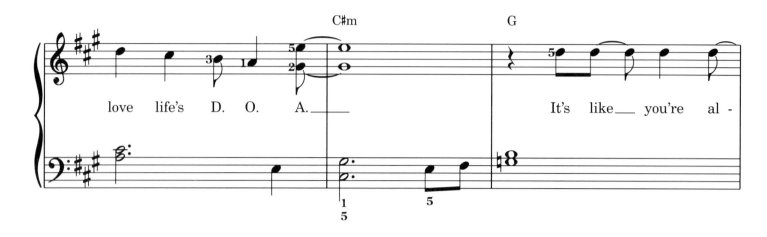

love life's D. O. A. _____ It's like_ you're al -

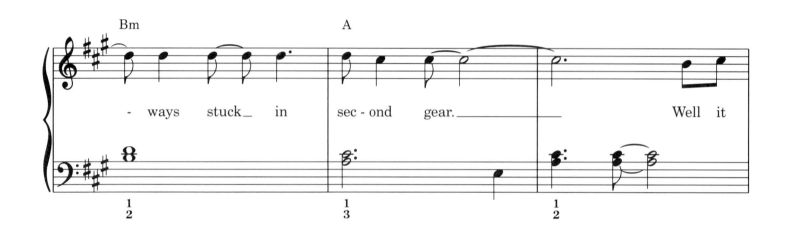

- ways stuck_ in sec - ond gear. _____ Well it

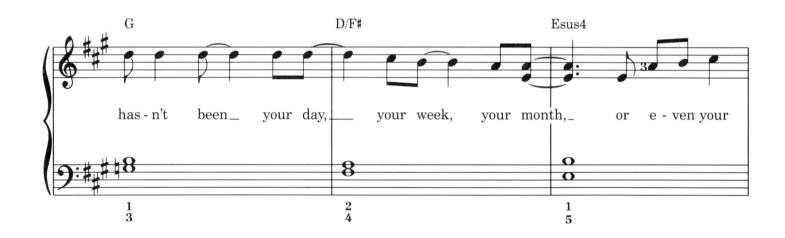

has - n't been_ your day,_ your week, your month,_ or e - ven your

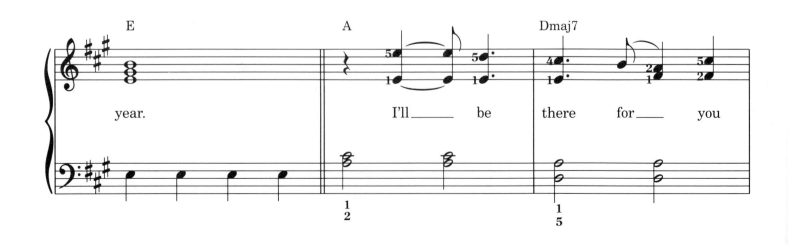

year. I'll_____ be there for ___ you

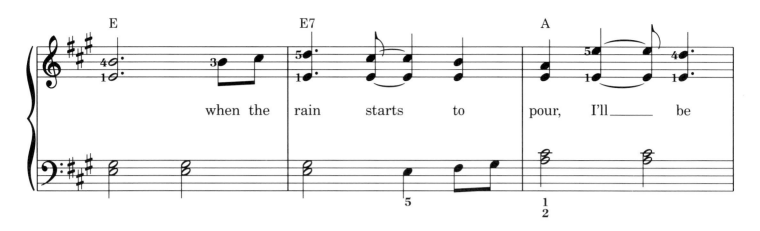

when the rain starts to pour, I'll____ be

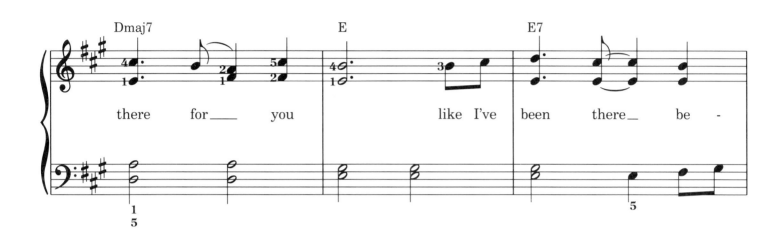

there for____ you like I've been there___ be -

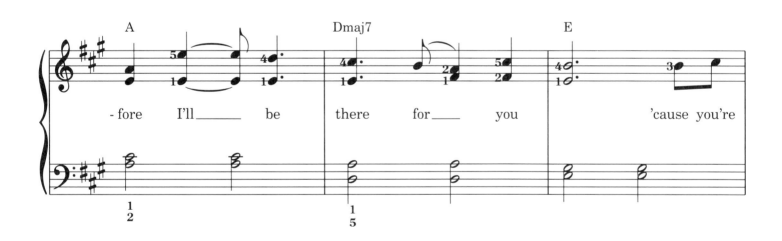

- fore I'll____ be there for____ you 'cause you're

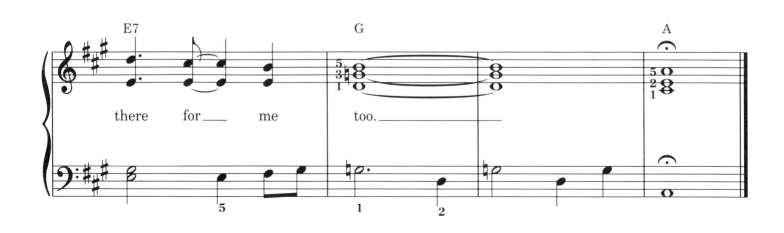

there for____ me too._____

GLADIATORS

Words and Music by
MUFF MURFIN

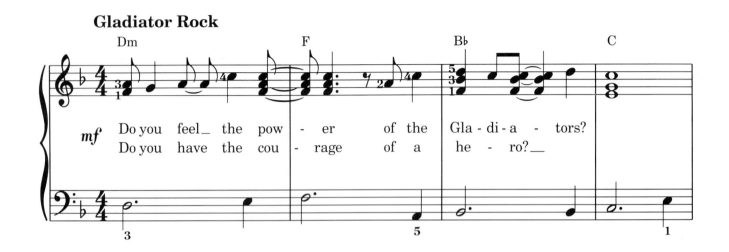

Do you feel_ the pow - er of the Gla - di - a - tors?
Do you have the cou - rage of a he - ro?__

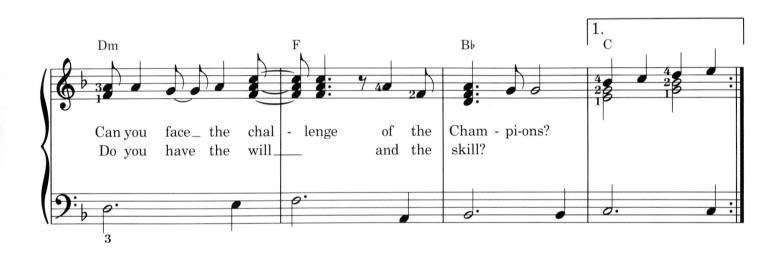

Can you face_ the chal - lenge of the Cham - pi-ons?
Do you have the will___ and the skill?

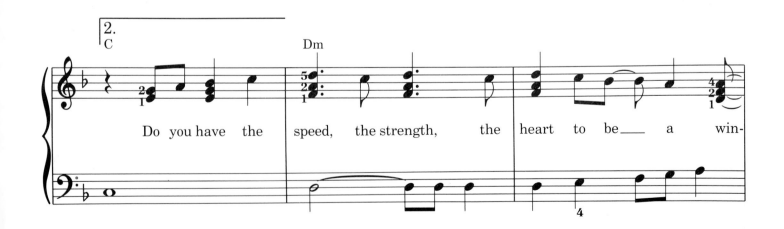

Do you have the speed, the strength, the heart to be_ a win-

-ner?___ It's not for___ be - gin - ners,

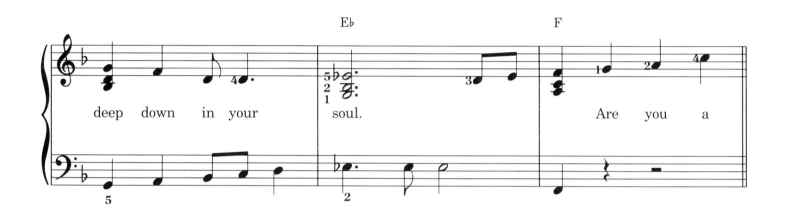

deep down in your soul. Are you a

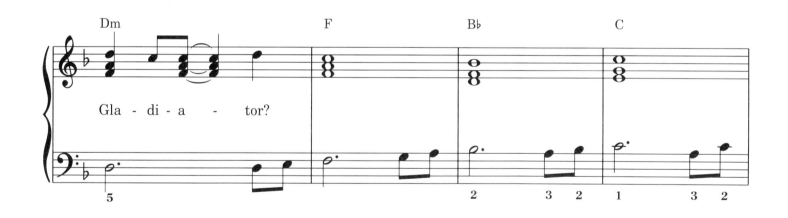

Gla - di - a - tor?

HAPPY DAYS

Words by NORMAN GIMBEL
Music by CHARLES FOX

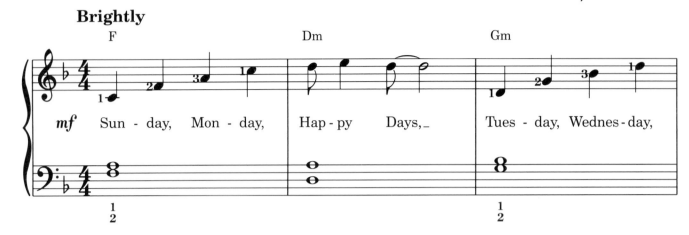

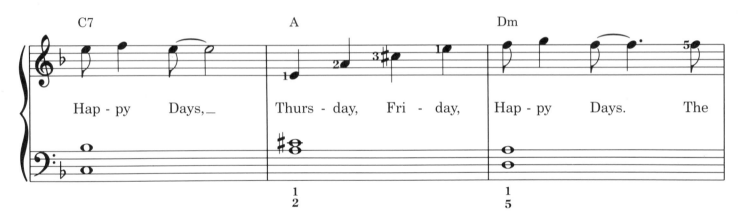

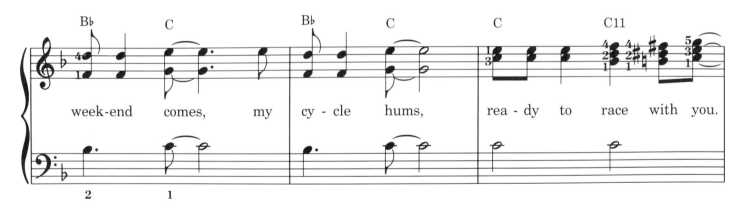

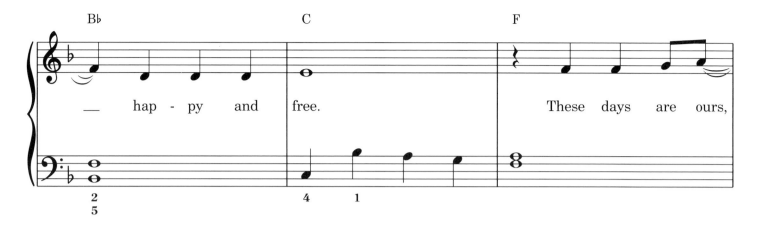

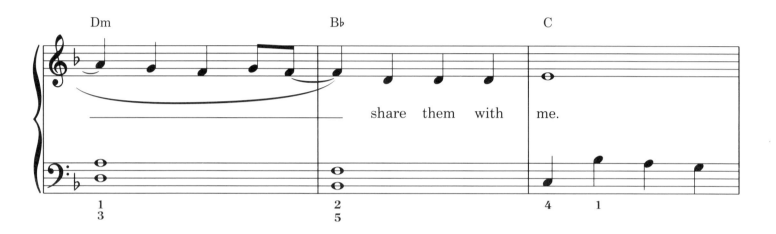

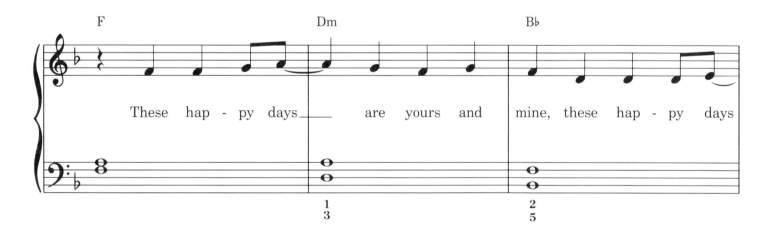

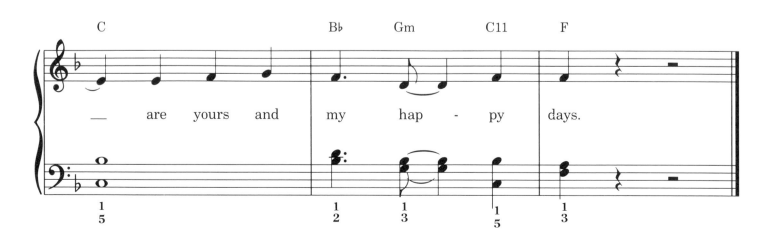

JUST WILLIAM

By NIGEL HESS

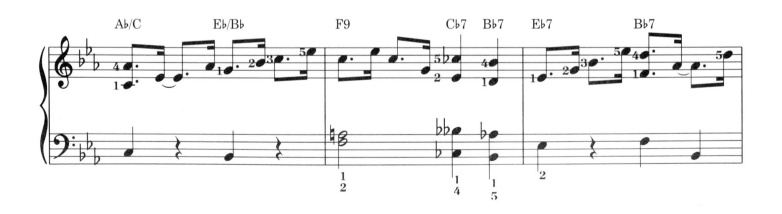

MATCH OF THE DAY

By RHET STOLLER

LAST OF THE SUMMER WINE

By RONNIE HAZLEHURST

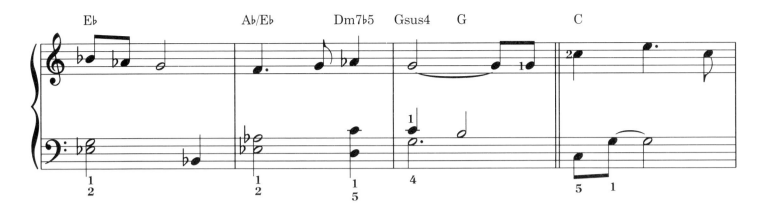

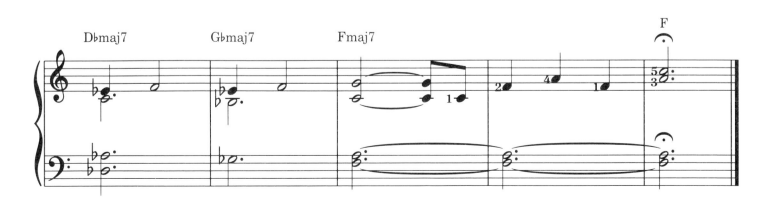

NEIGHBOURS

Words and Music by
TONY HATCH and JACKIE TRENT

ONLY FOOLS AND HORSES

Words and Music by
JOHN R SULLIVAN

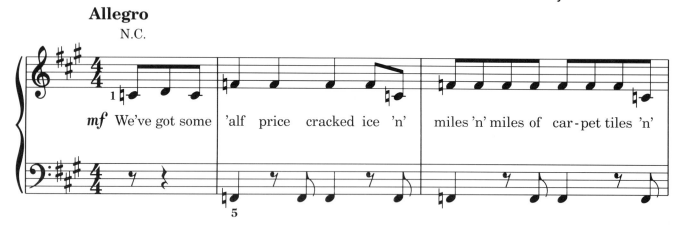

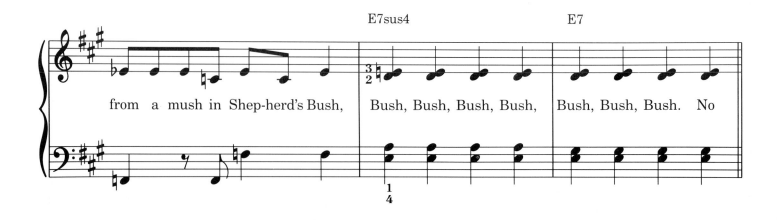

WYCLIFFE

By NIGEL HESS

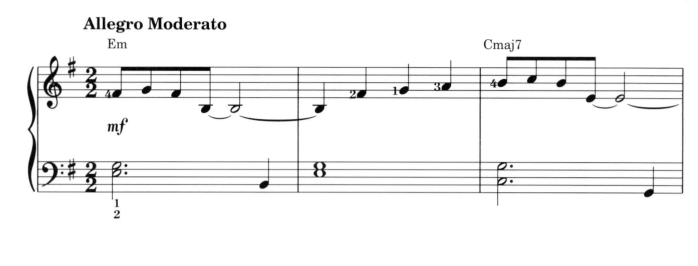

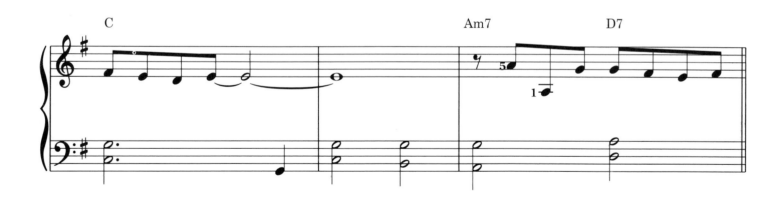

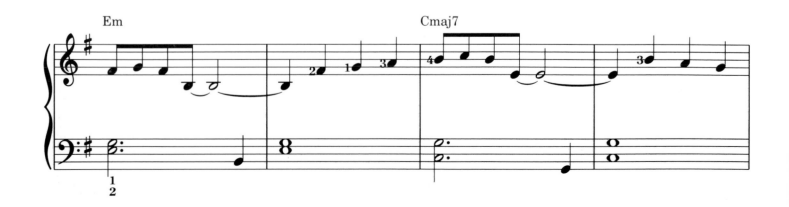

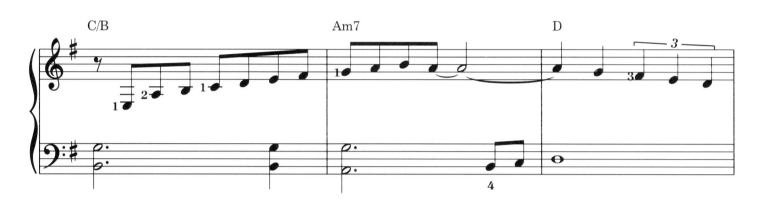

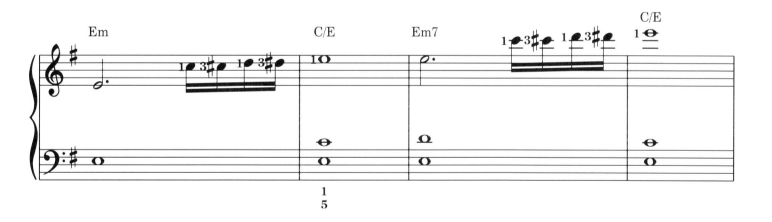

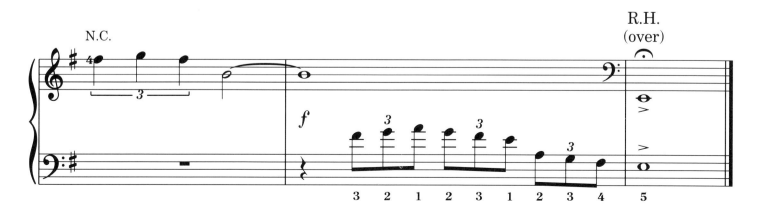

ROSEANNE
(Main Title)

Blues

By DANFORD FOLIART and PEARL HOWARD